FLIGHTS

- A LIFTOFF LOGBOOK -

POSTCARD

IF FOUND,
RETURN TO

All about me

NAME

HOMETOWN

1ST TRIP

1ST FLIGHT

FAVORITE PART OF TRAVELING

1ST TRAIN

FAVORITE TRIP

1ST BOAT

TRAVEL COMPANIONS

Packing Essentials

CLOTHING

Short Sleeve Shirts

Long Sleeve Shirts

Pants

Shorts

Dresses

Socks

Shoes

Sandals

Underwear

Hat

Swimsuit

Pajamas

Jacket

Hat & Gloves

_____

_____

TOILETRIES

Shampoo & Conditioner

Hairbrush

Soap

Toothpaste & Toothbrush

Sunscreen

_____

_____

_____

_____

MISCELLANEOUS

Money

Passport/ID

Book

Tablet & Charger

Phone & Charger

Headphones

Reusable Water Bottle

Snacks

Stuffed Animal

Small, Lightweight Toys

Glasses / Sunglasses

_____

_____

_____

_____

_____

_____

_____

_____

_____

_____

_____

_____

_____

Travel Photo Challenge

CAN YOU SNAP A PHOTO OF THESE BY THE END OF EACH TRIP?

- View from an airplane window
- A funny sign
- Food you've never seen before
- Something colorful
- Something sweet
- An animal
- Solo selfie
- Group selfie
- Someone you love, smiling
- Your feet
- A flower
- A reflection
- Sunrise or sunset
- Something you created
- Something unexpected
- Something you learned
- Something old
- Something new
- Something that reminded you of another person

Bucket List Experiences

WHAT GLOBAL EXPERIENCES DO YOU WANT TO COLLECT IN YOUR LIFETIME?

- [ ]
- [ ]
- [ ]
- [ ]
- [ ]
- [ ]
- [ ]
- [ ]
- [ ]
- [ ]
- [ ]
- [ ]
- [ ]
- [ ]
- [ ]
- [ ]
- [ ]
- [ ]
- [ ]
- [ ]
- [ ]
- [ ]
- [ ]

Bucket list Places

AUSTRALIA

WHAT NATURAL AREAS, LANDMARKS, OR CITIES DO YOU WANT TO EXPLORE?

BRAZIL

ITALY

- ☐
- ☐
- ☐
- ☐
- ☐
- ☐
- ☐
- ☐
- ☐
- ☐
- ☐
- ☐
- ☐
- ☐
- ☐
- ☐
- ☐
- ☐
- ☐
- ☐
- ☐
- ☐
- ☐
- ☐

★ INDIA ★

FRANCE

JAPAN

EGYPT

SEE "THE WORLD IN LISTS" ON PAGE 116 FOR INSPIRATION.

FINAL DESTINATION: _____

FLIGHT STATS

Date/Time: Aircraft Model:

✈ Departure Airport: Flight Distance:

✈ Arrival Airport: Flight Duration:

Airline & Flight #:   Pilot:

....

THINGS I'M LOOKING FORWARD TO:

I'M FEELING   I REMEMBERED TO HYDRATE

SOME GOOD THINGS

FLIGHT RATING

⭐ ⭐ ⭐ ⭐ ⭐

Favorite food consumed:

Name and hometown of a person near you:

Random act of kindness:

Best flight crew joke:

MESSAGES FROM THE FLIGHT CREW

TIME SPENT

Sleeping	
Eating	
Chatting	
Watching TV	
Studying	

FINAL DESTINATION: _____

FLIGHT STATS

Date/Time: Aircraft Model:

✈ Departure Airport: Flight Distance:

🛬 Arrival Airport: Flight Duration:

Airline & Flight #:   Pilot:

....

THINGS I'M LOOKING FORWARD TO:

....

I'M FEELING   ## I REMEMBERED TO HYDRATE

SOME GOOD THINGS

FLIGHT RATING

Favorite food consumed:

Name and hometown of a person near you:

Random act of kindness:

Best flight crew joke:

MESSAGES FROM THE FLIGHT CREW

TIME SPENT

Sleeping	
Eating	
Chatting	
Watching TV	
Studying	

FINAL DESTINATION: _____

FLIGHT STATS

Date/Time: Aircraft Model:

 Departure Airport: Flight Distance:

Arrival Airport: Flight Duration:

Airline & Flight #:   Pilot:

....

THINGS I'M LOOKING FORWARD TO:

....

I'M FEELING   I REMEMBERED TO HYDRATE

SOME GOOD THINGS

FLIGHT RATING

☆ ☆ ☆ ☆ ☆

Favorite food consumed:

Name and hometown of a person near you:

Random act of kindness:

Best flight crew joke:

MESSAGES FROM THE FLIGHT CREW

TIME SPENT

Sleeping	
Eating	
Chatting	
Watching TV	
Studying	

FINAL DESTINATION: _____

FLIGHT STATS

Date/Time: Aircraft Model:

✈ Departure Airport: Flight Distance:

✈ Arrival Airport: Flight Duration:

Airline & Flight #:   Pilot:

· ·

THINGS I'M LOOKING FORWARD TO:

· ·

I'M FEELING   ## I REMEMBERED TO HYDRATE

SOME GOOD THINGS

FLIGHT RATING

☆ ☆ ☆ ☆ ☆

Favorite food consumed:

Name and hometown of a person near you:

Random act of kindness:

Best flight crew joke:

MESSAGES FROM THE FLIGHT CREW

TIME SPENT

Sleeping	
Eating	
Chatting	
Watching TV	
Studying	

FINAL DESTINATION: _____

FLIGHT STATS

Date/Time: Aircraft Model:

 Departure Airport: Flight Distance:

Arrival Airport: Flight Duration:

Airline & Flight #:   Pilot:

THINGS I'M LOOKING FORWARD TO:

I'M FEELING   ## I REMEMBERED TO HYDRATE

SOME GOOD THINGS

FLIGHT RATING

Favorite food consumed:

Name and hometown of a person near you:

Random act of kindness:

Best flight crew joke:

MESSAGES FROM THE FLIGHT CREW

TIME SPENT

Sleeping	
Eating	
Chatting	
Watching TV	
Studying	

FINAL DESTINATION: _____

FLIGHT STATS

Date/Time: Aircraft Model:

✈ Departure Airport: Flight Distance:

✈ Arrival Airport: Flight Duration:

Airline & Flight #:   Pilot:

....

THINGS I'M LOOKING FORWARD TO:

I'M FEELING   I REMEMBERED TO HYDRATE

SOME GOOD THINGS

Favorite food consumed:

Name and hometown of a person near you:

Random act of kindness:

Best flight crew joke:

MESSAGES FROM THE FLIGHT CREW

TIME SPENT

Sleeping	
Eating	
Chatting	
Watching TV	
Studying	

FINAL DESTINATION: _____

FLIGHT STATS

Date/Time: Aircraft Model:

✈ Departure Airport: Flight Distance:

✈ Arrival Airport: Flight Duration:

Airline & Flight #:   Pilot:

THINGS I'M LOOKING FORWARD TO:

I'M FEELING   I REMEMBERED TO HYDRATE

SOME GOOD THINGS

FLIGHT RATING

⭐ ⭐ ⭐ ⭐ ⭐

Favorite food consumed:

Name and hometown of a person near you:

Random act of kindness:

Best flight crew joke:

MESSAGES FROM THE FLIGHT CREW

TIME SPENT

Sleeping	
Eating	
Chatting	
Watching TV	
Studying	

FINAL DESTINATION: _____

FLIGHT STATS

Date/Time: Aircraft Model:

✈ Departure Airport: Flight Distance:

✈ Arrival Airport: Flight Duration:

Airline & Flight #:   Pilot:

· ·

THINGS I'M LOOKING FORWARD TO:

· ·

I'M FEELING   ## I REMEMBERED TO HYDRATE

SOME GOOD THINGS

☆ ☆ ☆ ☆ ☆

Favorite food consumed:

Name and hometown of a person near you:

Random act of kindness:

Best flight crew joke:

MESSAGES FROM THE FLIGHT CREW

TIME SPENT

Sleeping	
Eating	
Chatting	
Watching TV	
Studying	

FINAL DESTINATION: _____

FLIGHT STATS

Date/Time: Aircraft Model:

✈ Departure Airport: Flight Distance:

✈ Arrival Airport: Flight Duration:

Airline & Flight #:   Pilot:

THINGS I'M LOOKING FORWARD TO:

I'M FEELING

I REMEMBERED TO HYDRATE

SOME GOOD THINGS

FLIGHT RATING

☆ ☆ ☆ ☆ ☆

Favorite food consumed:

Name and hometown of a person near you:

Random act of kindness:

Best flight crew joke:

MESSAGES FROM THE FLIGHT CREW

TIME SPENT

Sleeping	
Eating	
Chatting	
Watching TV	
Studying	

FINAL DESTINATION: _____

FLIGHT STATS

Date/Time: Aircraft Model:

✈ Departure Airport: Flight Distance:

✈ Arrival Airport: Flight Duration:

Airline & Flight #:   Pilot:

....

THINGS I'M LOOKING FORWARD TO:

....

I'M FEELING   I REMEMBERED TO HYDRATE

SOME GOOD THINGS

FLIGHT RATING

Favorite food consumed:

Name and hometown of a person near you:

Random act of kindness:

Best flight crew joke:

MESSAGES FROM THE FLIGHT CREW

TIME SPENT

Sleeping	
Eating	
Chatting	
Watching TV	
Studying	

FINAL DESTINATION: _____

FLIGHT STATS

Date/Time: Aircraft Model:

✈ Departure Airport: Flight Distance:

✈ Arrival Airport: Flight Duration:

Airline & Flight #:   Pilot:

THINGS I'M LOOKING FORWARD TO:

I'M FEELING   I REMEMBERED TO HYDRATE

SOME GOOD THINGS

FLIGHT RATING

☆ ☆ ☆ ☆ ☆

Favorite food consumed:

Name and hometown of a person near you:

Random act of kindness:

Best flight crew joke:

MESSAGES FROM THE FLIGHT CREW

TIME SPENT

Sleeping	
Eating	
Chatting	
Watching TV	
Studying	

FINAL DESTINATION: _____

FLIGHT STATS

Date/Time: Aircraft Model:

✈ Departure Airport: Flight Distance:

✈ Arrival Airport: Flight Duration:

Airline & Flight #:   Pilot:

. . . .

THINGS I'M LOOKING FORWARD TO:

. . . .

I'M FEELING   ## I REMEMBERED TO HYDRATE

SOME GOOD THINGS

FLIGHT RATING

☆ ☆ ☆ ☆ ☆

Favorite food consumed:

Name and hometown of a person near you:

Random act of kindness:

Best flight crew joke:

MESSAGES FROM THE FLIGHT CREW

TIME SPENT

Sleeping	
Eating	
Chatting	
Watching TV	
Studying	

FINAL DESTINATION: _____

FLIGHT STATS

Date/Time: Aircraft Model:

✈ Departure Airport: Flight Distance:

✈ Arrival Airport: Flight Duration:

Airline & Flight #:   Pilot:

....

THINGS I'M LOOKING FORWARD TO:

....

I'M FEELING   I REMEMBERED TO HYDRATE

SOME GOOD THINGS

FLIGHT RATING

☆ ☆ ☆ ☆ ☆

Favorite food consumed:

Name and hometown of a person near you:

Random act of kindness:

Best flight crew joke:

MESSAGES FROM THE FLIGHT CREW

TIME SPENT

Sleeping	
Eating	
Chatting	
Watching TV	
Studying	

FINAL DESTINATION: _____

FLIGHT STATS

Date/Time: Aircraft Model:

✈ Departure Airport: Flight Distance:

✈ Arrival Airport: Flight Duration:

Airline & Flight #:   Pilot:

THINGS I'M LOOKING FORWARD TO:

I'M FEELING   I REMEMBERED TO HYDRATE

SOME GOOD THINGS

FLIGHT RATING

Favorite food consumed:

Name and hometown of a person near you:

Random act of kindness:

Best flight crew joke:

MESSAGES FROM THE FLIGHT CREW

TIME SPENT

Sleeping	
Eating	
Chatting	
Watching TV	
Studying	

FINAL DESTINATION: _____

FLIGHT STATS

Date/Time: Aircraft Model:

✈ Departure Airport: Flight Distance:

✈ Arrival Airport: Flight Duration:

Airline & Flight #:   Pilot:

THINGS I'M LOOKING FORWARD TO:

I'M FEELING   I REMEMBERED TO HYDRATE

SOME GOOD THINGS

FLIGHT RATING

Favorite food consumed:

Name and hometown of a person near you:

Random act of kindness:

Best flight crew joke:

MESSAGES FROM THE FLIGHT CREW

TIME SPENT

Sleeping	
Eating	
Chatting	
Watching TV	
Studying	

FINAL DESTINATION: _____

FLIGHT STATS

Date/Time: Aircraft Model:

✈ Departure Airport: Flight Distance:

✈ Arrival Airport: Flight Duration:

Airline & Flight #:   Pilot:

THINGS I'M LOOKING FORWARD TO:

I'M FEELING   I REMEMBERED TO HYDRATE

SOME GOOD THINGS

FLIGHT RATING

Favorite food consumed:

Name and hometown of a person near you:

Random act of kindness:

Best flight crew joke:

MESSAGES FROM THE FLIGHT CREW

TIME SPENT

Sleeping	
Eating	
Chatting	
Watching TV	
Studying	

FINAL DESTINATION: _____

FLIGHT STATS

Date/Time:

✈ Departure Airport:

✈ Arrival Airport:

Airline & Flight #:

Aircraft Model:

Flight Distance:

Flight Duration:

Pilot:

THINGS I'M LOOKING FORWARD TO:

I'M FEELING

I REMEMBERED TO HYDRATE

SOME GOOD THINGS

FLIGHT RATING

Favorite food consumed:

Name and hometown of a person near you:

Random act of kindness:

Best flight crew joke:

MESSAGES FROM THE FLIGHT CREW

TIME SPENT

Sleeping	
Eating	
Chatting	
Watching TV	
Studying	

FINAL DESTINATION: _____

FLIGHT STATS

Date/Time: Aircraft Model:

✈ Departure Airport: Flight Distance:

✈ Arrival Airport: Flight Duration:

Airline & Flight #:   Pilot:

THINGS I'M LOOKING FORWARD TO:

I'M FEELING   I REMEMBERED TO HYDRATE

SOME GOOD THINGS

Favorite food consumed:

Name and hometown of a person near you:

Random act of kindness:

Best flight crew joke:

MESSAGES FROM THE FLIGHT CREW

TIME SPENT

Sleeping	
Eating	
Chatting	
Watching TV	
Studying	

FINAL DESTINATION: _____

FLIGHT STATS

Date/Time: Aircraft Model:

✈ Departure Airport: Flight Distance:

✈ Arrival Airport: Flight Duration:

Airline & Flight #:   Pilot:

THINGS I'M LOOKING FORWARD TO:

I'M FEELING   I REMEMBERED TO HYDRATE

SOME GOOD THINGS

FLIGHT RATING

☆ ☆ ☆ ☆ ☆

Favorite food consumed:

Name and hometown of a person near you:

Random act of kindness:

Best flight crew joke:

MESSAGES FROM THE FLIGHT CREW

TIME SPENT

Sleeping	
Eating	
Chatting	
Watching TV	
Studying	

FINAL DESTINATION: _____

FLIGHT STATS

Date/Time: Aircraft Model:

✈ Departure Airport: Flight Distance:

✈ Arrival Airport: Flight Duration:

Airline & Flight #:   Pilot:

THINGS I'M LOOKING FORWARD TO:

I'M FEELING   I REMEMBERED TO HYDRATE

SOME GOOD THINGS

FLIGHT RATING

Favorite food consumed:

Name and hometown of a person near you:

Random act of kindness:

Best flight crew joke:

MESSAGES FROM THE FLIGHT CREW

TIME SPENT

Sleeping	
Eating	
Chatting	
Watching TV	
Studying	

FINAL DESTINATION: _____

FLIGHT STATS

Date/Time: Aircraft Model:

✈ Departure Airport: Flight Distance:

✈ Arrival Airport: Flight Duration:

Airline & Flight #:   Pilot:

THINGS I'M LOOKING FORWARD TO:

I'M FEELING   I REMEMBERED TO HYDRATE

SOME GOOD THINGS

FLIGHT RATING

Favorite food consumed:

Name and hometown of a person near you:

Random act of kindness:

Best flight crew joke:

MESSAGES FROM THE FLIGHT CREW

TIME SPENT

Sleeping	
Eating	
Chatting	
Watching TV	
Studying	

FINAL DESTINATION: _____

FLIGHT STATS

Date/Time: Aircraft Model:

✈ Departure Airport: Flight Distance:

✈ Arrival Airport: Flight Duration:

Airline & Flight #:   Pilot:

THINGS I'M LOOKING FORWARD TO:

I'M FEELING   I REMEMBERED TO HYDRATE

SOME GOOD THINGS

FLIGHT RATING

Favorite food consumed:

Name and hometown of a person near you:

Random act of kindness:

Best flight crew joke:

MESSAGES FROM THE FLIGHT CREW

TIME SPENT

Sleeping	
Eating	
Chatting	
Watching TV	
Studying	

FINAL DESTINATION: _____

FLIGHT STATS

Date/Time: Aircraft Model:

✈ Departure Airport: Flight Distance:

✈ Arrival Airport: Flight Duration:

Airline & Flight #:   Pilot:

THINGS I'M LOOKING FORWARD TO:

I'M FEELING   I REMEMBERED TO HYDRATE

SOME GOOD THINGS

FLIGHT RATING

Favorite food consumed:

Name and hometown of a person near you:

Random act of kindness:

Best flight crew joke:

MESSAGES FROM THE FLIGHT CREW

TIME SPENT

Sleeping	
Eating	
Chatting	
Watching TV	
Studying	

FINAL DESTINATION: _____

FLIGHT STATS

Date/Time: Aircraft Model:

✈ Departure Airport: Flight Distance:

✈ Arrival Airport: Flight Duration:

Airline & Flight #:   Pilot:

THINGS I'M LOOKING FORWARD TO:

I'M FEELING   I REMEMBERED TO HYDRATE

SOME GOOD THINGS

FLIGHT RATING

Favorite food consumed:

Name and hometown of a person near you:

Random act of kindness:

Best flight crew joke:

MESSAGES FROM THE FLIGHT CREW

TIME SPENT

Sleeping	
Eating	
Chatting	
Watching TV	
Studying	

FINAL DESTINATION: _____

FLIGHT STATS

Date/Time: Aircraft Model:

✈ Departure Airport: Flight Distance:

✈ Arrival Airport: Flight Duration:

Airline & Flight #:   Pilot:

....

THINGS I'M LOOKING FORWARD TO:

I'M FEELING   I REMEMBERED TO HYDRATE

SOME GOOD THINGS

Favorite food consumed:

Name and hometown of a person near you:

Random act of kindness:

Best flight crew joke:

MESSAGES FROM THE FLIGHT CREW

TIME SPENT

Sleeping	
Eating	
Chatting	
Watching TV	
Studying	

FINAL DESTINATION: _____

FLIGHT STATS

Date/Time: Aircraft Model:

✈ Departure Airport: Flight Distance:

✈ Arrival Airport: Flight Duration:

Airline & Flight #:   Pilot:

THINGS I'M LOOKING FORWARD TO:

I'M FEELING   I REMEMBERED TO HYDRATE

SOME GOOD THINGS

FLIGHT RATING

Favorite food consumed:

Name and hometown of a person near you:

Random act of kindness:

Best flight crew joke:

MESSAGES FROM THE FLIGHT CREW

TIME SPENT

Sleeping	
Eating	
Chatting	
Watching TV	
Studying	

Flight Distance Tracker

Date	Flight	From/To	Distance

SUBTOTAL

Flight Distance Tracker

Date	Flight	From/To	Distance

SUBTOTAL

Flight Distance Tracker

Date	Flight	From/To	Distance

SUBTOTAL

Flight Distance Tracker

Date	Flight	From/To	Distance

SUBTOTAL

The World in lists

CONTINENTS
Asia
Africa
North America
South America
Antarctica
Europe
Australia

OCEANS
Arctic Ocean
Atlantic Ocean
Indian Ocean
Pacific Ocean
Southern Ocean

TALLEST MOUNTAINS
Everest - Nepal & Tibet
K2 (Chogori or Godwin-Austin) - Pakistan & China
Kanchenjunga - Nepal, India & Sikkim
Lhotse - Nepal & Tibet
Makalu - Nepal & Tibet
Cho Oyu - Nepal
Dhaulagiri I - Nepal
Manaslu - Nepal
Nanga Parbat - Pakistan
Annapurna I - Nepal

LONGEST RIVERS
Nile - Tanzania, Uganda, Sudan & Egypt
Amazon - Brazil
Mississippi-Missouri-Red Rock - USA
Yenisey-Angara-Selenga - Russia & Mongolia
Yangtze - China
Ob'-Irtysh - China, Kazakhstan & Russia
Huang Ho - China
Zaire - Congo
Lena-Kirenga - Russia
Amur-Argun - Russia & China

7 WONDERS OF THE MODERN WORLD

Machu Picchu - Peru
Chichén Itzá - Mexico
Roman Colosseum - Italy
Christ the Redeemer - Brazil
The Great Wall of China
The Taj Mahal - India
The City of Petra - Jordan

7 WONDERS OF THE NATURAL WORLD

Mount Everest - Between Nepal & Tibet
Paricutin Volcano - Mexico
The Grand Canyon - USA
Victoria Falls - Zambia
The Harbor Of Rio de Janeiro - Brazil
Great Barrier Reef - Australia
Northern Lights

7 WONDERS OF THE ANCIENT WORLD

Great Pyramid of Giza (The only Ancient Wonder that still exists)
Hanging Gardens of Babylon
Statue of Zeus
Temple of Artemis
Mausoleum of Halicarnassus
Pharos (Lighthouse) of Alexandria
Colossus of Rhodes

The World in lists

STATES IN THE UNITED STATES

☐ Alabama
☐ Alaska
☐ Arizona
☐ Arkansas
☐ California
☐ Colorado
☐ Connecticut
☐ Delaware
☐ Florida
☐ Georgia
☐ Hawaii
☐ Idaho
☐ Illinois
☐ Indiana
☐ Iowa
☐ Kansas
☐ Kentucky
☐ Louisiana
☐ Maine
☐ Maryland
☐ Massachusetts
☐ Michigan
☐ Minnesota
☐ Mississippi
☐ Missouri

☐ Montana
☐ Nebraska
☐ Nevada
☐ New Hampshire
☐ New Jersey
☐ New Mexico
☐ New York
☐ North Carolina
☐ North Dakota
☐ Ohio
☐ Oklahoma
☐ Oregon
☐ Pennsylvania
☐ Rhode Island
☐ South Carolina
☐ South Dakota
☐ Tennessee
☐ Texas
☐ Utah
☐ Vermont
☐ Virginia
☐ Washington
☐ West Virginia
☐ Wisconsin
☐ Wyoming

The World in lists

COUNTRIES IN AFRICA

- ☐ Algeria
- ☐ Angola
- ☐ Benin
- ☐ Botswana
- ☐ Burkina Faso
- ☐ Burundi
- ☐ Cabo Verde
- ☐ Cameroon
- ☐ Central African Republic
- ☐ Chad
- ☐ Comoros
- ☐ Congo, Democratic Republic
- ☐ Congo, Republic
- ☐ Cote d'Ivoire
- ☐ Djibouti
- ☐ Egypt
- ☐ Equatorial Guinea
- ☐ Eritrea
- ☐ Eswatini
- ☐ Ethiopia
- ☐ Gabon
- ☐ Gambia
- ☐ Ghana
- ☐ Guinea
- ☐ Guinea-Bissau
- ☐ Kenya
- ☐ Lesotho
- ☐ Liberia
- ☐ Libya
- ☐ Madagascar
- ☐ Malawi
- ☐ Mali
- ☐ Mauritania
- ☐ Mauritius
- ☐ Morocco
- ☐ Mozambique
- ☐ Namibia
- ☐ Niger
- ☐ Nigeria
- ☐ Rwanda
- ☐ Sao Tome & Principe
- ☐ Senegal
- ☐ Seychelles
- ☐ Sierra Leone
- ☐ Somalia
- ☐ South Africa
- ☐ South Sudan
- ☐ Sudan
- ☐ Tanzania
- ☐ Togo
- ☐ Tunisia
- ☐ Uganda
- ☐ Zambia
- ☐ Zimbabwe

COUNTRIES IN ASIA

- [ ] Afghanistan
- [ ] Armenia
- [ ] Azerbaijan
- [ ] Bahrain
- [ ] Bangladesh
- [ ] Bhutan
- [ ] Brunei
- [ ] Cambodia
- [ ] China
- [ ] Cyprus
- [ ] East Timor
- [ ] Egypt
- [ ] Georgia
- [ ] India
- [ ] Indonesia
- [ ] Iran
- [ ] Iraq
- [ ] Israel
- [ ] Japan
- [ ] Jordan
- [ ] Kazakhstan
- [ ] Kuwait
- [ ] Kyrgyzstan
- [ ] Laos
- [ ] Lebanon
- [ ] Malaysia
- [ ] Maldives
- [ ] Mongolia
- [ ] Myanmar
- [ ] Nepal
- [ ] North Korea
- [ ] Oman
- [ ] Pakistan
- [ ] Palestine
- [ ] Philippines
- [ ] Qatar
- [ ] Russia
- [ ] Saudi Arabia
- [ ] Singapore
- [ ] South Korea
- [ ] Sri Lanka
- [ ] Syria
- [ ] Taiwan
- [ ] Tajikistan
- [ ] Thailand
- [ ] Turkey
- [ ] Turkmenistan
- [ ] United Arab Emirates
- [ ] Uzbekistan
- [ ] Vietnam
- [ ] Yemen

The World in lists

COUNTRIES IN EUROPE

- ☐ Albania
- ☐ Andorra
- ☐ Armenia
- ☐ Austria
- ☐ Azerbaijan
- ☐ Belarus
- ☐ Belgium
- ☐ Bosnia & Herzegovina
- ☐ Bulgaria
- ☐ Croatia
- ☐ Cyprus
- ☐ Czechia
- ☐ Denmark
- ☐ Estonia
- ☐ Finland
- ☐ France
- ☐ Georgia
- ☐ Germany
- ☐ Greece
- ☐ Hungary
- ☐ Iceland
- ☐ Ireland
- ☐ Italy
- ☐ Kazakhstan
- ☐ Kosovo
- ☐ Latvia
- ☐ Liechtenstein
- ☐ Lithuania
- ☐ Luxembourg
- ☐ Malta
- ☐ Moldova
- ☐ Monaco
- ☐ Montenegro
- ☐ Netherlands
- ☐ North Macedonia
- ☐ Norway
- ☐ Poland
- ☐ Portugal
- ☐ Romania
- ☐ Russia
- ☐ San Marino
- ☐ Serbia
- ☐ Slovakia
- ☐ Slovenia
- ☐ Spain
- ☐ Sweden
- ☐ Switzerland
- ☐ Turkey
- ☐ Ukraine
- ☐ UK: England
- ☐ UK: Northern Ireland
- ☐ UK: Scotland
- ☐ UK: Wales
- ☐ Vatican City

COUNTRIES IN NORTH AMERICA

- ☐ Antigua & Barbuda
- ☐ Bahamas
- ☐ Barbados
- ☐ Belize
- ☐ Canada
- ☐ Costa Rica
- ☐ Cuba
- ☐ Dominica
- ☐ Dominican Republic
- ☐ El Salvador
- ☐ Grenada
- ☐ Guatemala
- ☐ Haiti
- ☐ Honduras
- ☐ Jamaica
- ☐ Mexico
- ☐ Nicaragua
- ☐ Panama
- ☐ Saint Kitts & Nevis
- ☐ Saint Lucia
- ☐ Saint Vincent & the Grenadines
- ☐ Trinidad & Tobago
- ☐ United States of America

COUNTRIES IN OCEANIA

- ☐ Australia
- ☐ Fiji
- ☐ Kiribati
- ☐ Marshall Islands
- ☐ Micronesia
- ☐ Nauru
- ☐ New Zealand
- ☐ Palau
- ☐ Papua New Guinea
- ☐ Samoa
- ☐ Solomon Islands
- ☐ Tonga
- ☐ Tuvalu
- ☐ Vanuatu

COUNTRIES IN SOUTH AMERICA

- ☐ Argentina
- ☐ Bolivia
- ☐ Brazil
- ☐ Chile
- ☐ Colombia
- ☐ Ecuador
- ☐ Guyana
- ☐ Paraguay
- ☐ Peru
- ☐ Suriname
- ☐ Uruguay
- ☐ Venezuela

The World in lists

TERRITORIES & DEPENDENCIES

- ☐ American Samoa | USA
- ☐ Anguilla | UK
- ☐ Aruba | Netherlands
- ☐ Ashmore & Cartier Islands | Australia
- ☐ Baker & Howland Islands | USA
- ☐ Bermuda | UK
- ☐ Bouvet Island | Norway
- ☐ British Indian Ocean Territory | UK
- ☐ British Virgin Islands | UK
- ☐ Cayman Islands | UK
- ☐ Christmas Island | Australia
- ☐ Cocos Islands | Australia
- ☐ Cook Islands | New Zealand
- ☐ Coral Sea Islands | Australia
- ☐ Faeroe Islands | Denmark
- ☐ Falkland Islands | UK
- ☐ French Guiana | France
- ☐ French Polynesia | France
- ☐ Gibraltar | UK
- ☐ Greenland | Denmark
- ☐ Guadeloupe | France
- ☐ Guam | USA
- ☐ Guernsey | UK
- ☐ Heard & Mc Donald Islands | Australia
- ☐ Hong Kong | Controlled by China
- ☐ Isle of Man | UK
- ☐ Jan Mayen | Norway
- ☐ Jarvis Island | USA

- ☐ Jersey | UK
- ☐ Johnston Atoll | USA
- ☐ Kingman Reef | USA
- ☐ Macao | Controlled by China
- ☐ Martinique | France
- ☐ Mayotte | France
- ☐ Midway Islands | USA
- ☐ Monteserrat | UK
- ☐ Navassa Island | USA
- ☐ Netherlands Antilles | Netherlands
- ☐ New Caledonia | France
- ☐ Niue | New Zealand
- ☐ Norfolk Island | Australia
- ☐ Northern Mariana Islands | USA
- ☐ Palmyra Atoll | USA
- ☐ Paracel Islands | disputed by Asian countries
- ☐ Puerto Rico | USA
- ☐ Peter Island | Norway
- ☐ Pitcairn Islands | UK
- ☐ Reunion | France
- ☐ St. Helena & Dependencies | UK
- ☐ St. Pierre & Miquelon | France
- ☐ South Georgia & South Sandwich Islands | UK
- ☐ Spratly Islands | disputed by Asian countries
- ☐ Svlabard | Norway
- ☐ Tokelau | New Zealand
- ☐ Turks & Caicos Islands | UK
- ☐ Virgin Islands | USA
- ☐ Wake Island | USA
- ☐ Wallis & Futuna | France

The Family Behind This Book

We are Catherine and Troy, based in Milwaukee, Wisconsin, USA. We share our love of traveling the world with our sons, Liam and Noah.

Aspiring to document memories, we began mailing postcards to our own home. This tradition became our inspiration when we launched *Postcard Narrative*.

Our travel experiences taught us journeys are half the fun and we sought a way to creatively archive them. For this reason, we created the Liftoff Logbook, a journal for your family and ours to capture travel dreams and adventures that begin above the clouds.

For memorable and affordable family trip ideas,
and our tips for traveling the world, visit
www.postcardnarrative.com

Tag us on Instagram and let us know where you're headed! We enjoy connecting with others who explore near and far.

POSTCARD_NARRATIVE

Made in the USA
Monee, IL
05 March 2023

29204868R00070